BrAiN BENDERS

THAT'S AMAZING

Thanks to the creative team:

Senior Editor: Alice Peebles

Designer: Bryony Anne Warren

and Collaborate Agency

First published in Great Britain in 2015 by
Hungry Tomato Ltd
PO Box 181
Edenbridge
Kent, TN8 9DP

A CIP catalogue record for this book is available from the British Library.

ISBN 978-1-910684-061

Printed and bound in China

Discover more at www.hungrytomato.com

THAT'S
AMAZING

by Dr. Gareth Moore

HUNGRY
TOMATO™

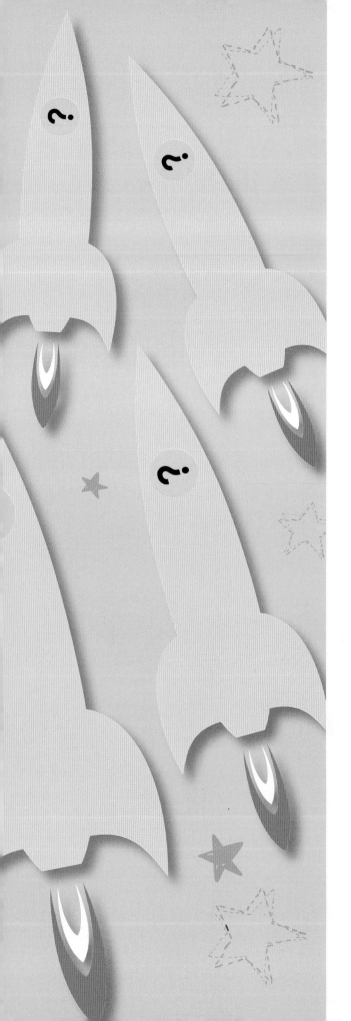

Contents

That's Amazing

Are you a wizard with words? A ninja with numbers? It's time to show your skills, using this book packed with numeric and word-based challenges.

You'll need to think smart and reason cleverly to solve all of the puzzles, but if you need help at any time then just turn to the 'Tips' section at the back of the book for some helpful hints. There are also solutions for checking your answers, if you need to.

So get your thinking cap on and turn the page! Have fun!

Riddle me this

This is a simple riddle to start your brain working:

What occurs once in a minute, twice in a moment but not once in a thousand years?

Need help with solving these puzzles? Turn to pages 26 to 28 for helpful tips.

Numbers and Reasoning

If you only know numbers and maths from school lessons, you might think that it's all hard work and difficult sums. But the truth is that maths is full of interesting patterns and tricks, and numbers can be just as much fun to play with as anything else!

1 Tricks with numbers

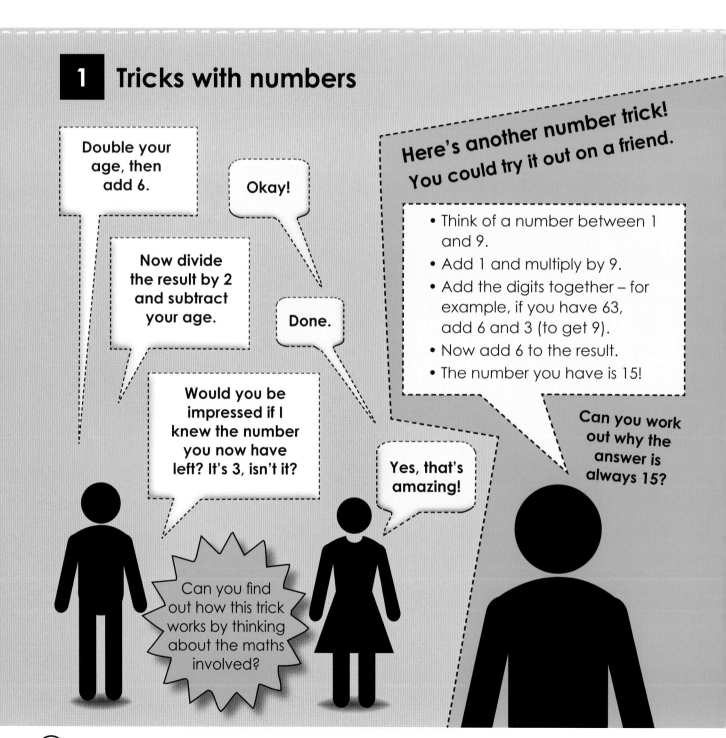

Double your age, then add 6.

Okay!

Now divide the result by 2 and subtract your age.

Done.

Would you be impressed if I knew the number you now have left? It's 3, isn't it?

Yes, that's amazing!

Can you find out how this trick works by thinking about the maths involved?

Here's another number trick! You could try it out on a friend.

- Think of a number between 1 and 9.
- Add 1 and multiply by 9.
- Add the digits together – for example, if you have 63, add 6 and 3 (to get 9).
- Now add 6 to the result.
- The number you have is 15!

Can you work out why the answer is always 15?

2 Pouring problem

You have three water containers, each of a different size.

Container **A** holds 3 litres, container **B** holds 5 litres and container **C** holds 8 litres.

A and **B** are both empty but **C** is filled to the brim with 8 litres of water.

How can you pour this water from one container to another so as to end up with exactly 4 litres of water in both **B** and **C**?

Doing it by eye is not the solution – there is a numerically precise method to find.

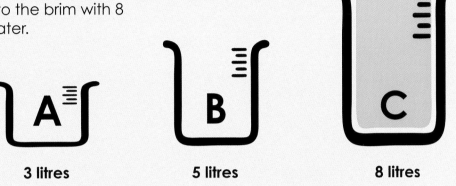

3 litres **5 litres** **8 litres**

3 River crossing

Can you solve this classic puzzle?

"A man wants to cross a river with his dog, his cat and a bowl of cat food. The problem is that he has to use a ferry to cross, and the ferryman will only let him bring one item at a time across the river per trip. If he leaves the dog alone with the cat on either side of the river, the cat will get scared and run away. If he leaves the cat alone with the cat food, the cat will eat the food."

How can the man get all three across the river, without the cat either running away or eating the food? You need to work out the correct sequence of ferry journeys.

Need help with solving these puzzles? Turn to pages 26 to 28 for helpful tips.

Number Manipulation

Are you good at solving number puzzles? On these pages you'll look for patterns in numbers, try some mathematical anagrams and practise some of your mental arithmetic skills.

1 Number anagrams

By rearranging all of these numbers and maths signs, can you work out how to reach each of the given totals?

For example, you could make 17 by doing this: 2 x 5 + 7 = 17.

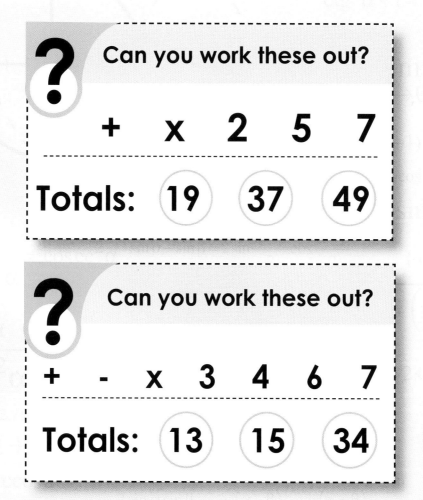

Can you work these out?

+   x   2   5   7

Totals: 19   37   49

Can you work these out?

+   -   x   3   4   6   7

Totals: 13   15   34

2 | Number sequences

Can you work out what number comes next in each countdown sequence? The first one is done for you as an example.

27 23 19 15 11 7 **?**

1 3 5 7 9 11 13
Add 2 at each step

1 2 4 8 16 32 **?**

2 5 8 11 14 17 **?**

1 2 3 5 8 13 **?**

3 | Brain chains

Start with the number on the left of each chain and follow each arrow in turn, applying each given maths operation as you go. For example, in the first chain you begin with 9, subtract 2, multiply by 7, and then so on until you reach the end of the chain. Do this without making any written notes – see if you can solve the whole chain in your head. If you find this too easy, try to solve each one in less than half a minute for an extra challenge!

9 — -2 — x7 — +3 — -4 — ÷8 — =?

17 — -14 — x4 — ÷3 — x12 — -11 — =?

12 — +16 — ÷4 — x5 — ÷7 — x8 — =?

Need help with solving these puzzles? Turn to pages 26 to 28 for helpful tips.

Find the Numbers

These challenges involve finding out which numbers will solve each problem. You can do this either by working everything out on paper or just guessing. Each guess that is not the right answer to a problem will often guide you a bit closer to the correct answer, so it's not always a bad way to work things out!

1 How old?

A mother is asked how old each of her three children is, and she says:

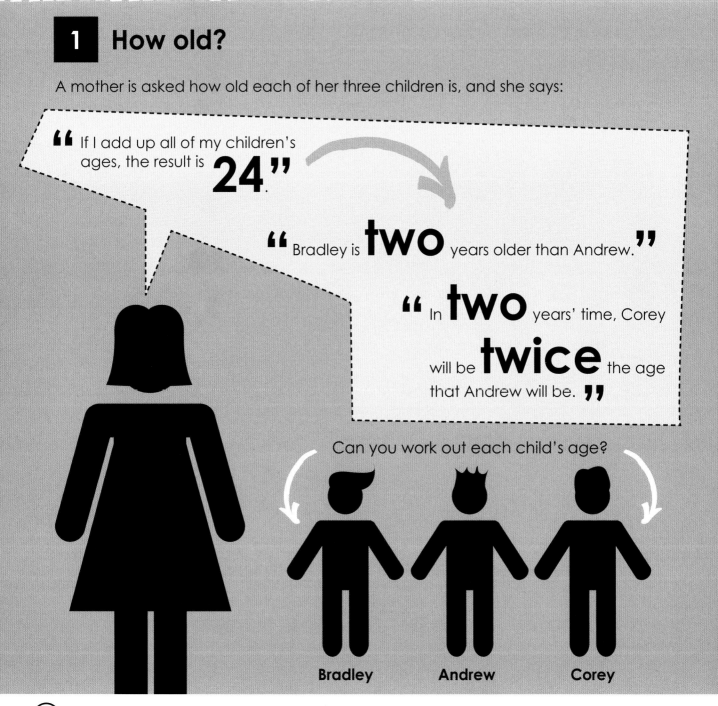

"If I add up all of my children's ages, the result is **24**."

"Bradley is **two** years older than Andrew."

"In **two** years' time, Corey will be **twice** the age that Andrew will be."

Can you work out each child's age?

Bradley   Andrew   Corey

2 Street map

Look at the following drawing of three houses on a street, showing the number of each house. Can you work out which house each child lives at, given the following clues?

• Five children live in the three houses pictured. Their names are Dan, Eliza, Frankie, Gayatri and Hayden.

• If you add the house number where Eliza lives to the house number where Dan lives you get 12.

• The total of the house numbers for Frankie, Hayden and Dan is 19.

• The total of the house numbers for Hayden, Gayatri, Eliza and Dan is 26.

• The total of the house numbers for Gayatri and Eliza is 14.

Dan Eliza Frankie Gayatri Hayden

3 Balloon bursting

Which of these balloons would you burst in order to leave only balloons that add up to the following totals?

44 35 19 18

Need help with solving these puzzles? Turn to pages 26 to 28 for helpful tips.

Amazing Numbers

There are lots of clever things you can do with numbers, from working things out with sneaky maths tricks to making up codes for sending secret messages.

1 Secret code

There are lots of ways to use numbers to hide secret messages. Perhaps the easiest way is to convert each letter to a number representing its position in the alphabet. A=1, B=2 and so on: Using this code, can you work out what this message says?

2 Super-secret code

To make your message more secure, you can change the numbers in some way. For example, you could number the alphabet backwards so that Z=1 and A=26. Or you could reverse the digits, so instead of writing 13 for M you would write 31. Using both of these changes – writing digits in reverse order, and numbering letters from Z=1 to A=26 – what does this message say?

42	21	32	22

42	9	62	42	61	22	32

3 Ultra-secret code

In real-world codes, the way that a letter is encoded usually depends not just on the letter itself but on the letters that come before it, which can make it extremely difficult to crack a code without knowing exactly what it says in advance. Here's an example of an ultra-secret code where each encoded number depends on the number before it! Let's start with just the super-secret code from below, so if we wanted to encode 'ZOOM' we would get:

1	21	21	41

Now to make it ultra-secret we can add the value of the previous number onto each number. So we have 1, 21+1, 21+21 and 41+21:

1	22	42	62

This makes your secret message really hidden, because now each 'O' has a different value – it's almost impossible for someone to guess what this says! In fact, can you decode this code yourself? You know how to encode it, so can you work out how to decode it? What day of the week is written here?

7	13	28	30	40	94	64

Two's a crowd

Is 186 a multiple of 2? You probably already know how to work out if a number is a multiple of 2. It's easy: if the last digit is even (0, 2, 4, 6, 8), the number is a multiple of 2. So 186 is a multiple of 2 because 6 is even. If you want, you can also check by working out that 186 = 2 x 93.

Easy threesy

Is 186 a multiple of 3? You can answer this question really quickly with this cunning trick: add the digits of a number (so 1 + 8 + 6 = 15 in this case), and if the answer is a multiple of 3, then so is the original number! 15 = 5 x 3, so 186 is a multiple of 3.

Four score

Is 516 a multiple of 4? Checking for multiples of 4 is a bit more tricky. You need to work out if the last two digits are a multiple of 4. So you need to know your times tables as far as 24 x 4 = 96 to use this trick! If the last two digits are a multiple of 4, then so is the full number. This does mean you can tell right away that 516 is a multiple of 4, because 16 is 4 x 4. You should ignore any leading zeroes, so you know that 608 is a multiple of 4 because you read 08 as 8, and 8 is 2 x 4. You also need to remember, or learn, that 0 itself is also a multiple of 4 because 0 x 4 (no 4s!) is 0 – therefore 700 is also a multiple of 4.

Five star

Any number that ends in '5' or '0' is a multiple of 5. Easy!

Six times table

How do you tell if a number is a multiple of 6? You just combine the tricks for seeing if it is a multiple of 2 and a multiple of 3. So if it ends in an even number, and the digits add up to a multiple of 3, then it is also a multiple of 6. Not that hard!

You try it!

Work these out without a calculator, using the above tricks! I bet if you'd been asked to do this before reading the instructions above, you'd have said it was impossible!

- Is 31,753 a multiple of 2?
- Is 938,676 a multiple of 3?
- Is 586,924 a multiple of 4?
- Is 18,484,830 a multiple of 5?
- Is 17,849,253 a multiple of 6?

Need help with solving these puzzles? Turn to pages 26 to 28 for helpful tips.

Open to Interpretation

Have you ever had a dream? Did you remember it? The chances are that you're really creative when you're dreaming, and there's no reason why you can't be just as creative when you're awake. Sometimes it's hard to think up ideas, but usually if you have something to get you started, then it's not so bad. This page has various techniques that can help trigger wacky thoughts, so if you ever need to think up your own creative ideas, you can use these tricks to get going!

1 Hidden in plain sight

Look at this picture below, top left. It looks like a plain white rectangle with a small black dot in it. But is it really? It could easily be a picture of a polar bear in a snow-storm! All you can see is its nose. What creative explanations can you come up with for these other pictures? There are no wrong answers!

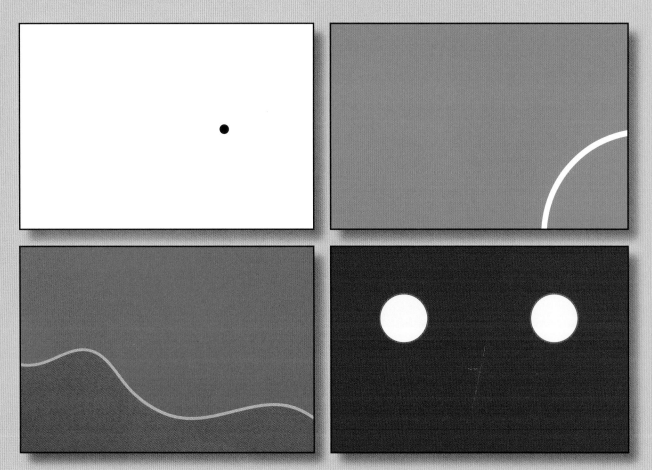

2   But what's it for?

Have you ever sat in class and played idly with the items on your desk to see what you can do with them? You can use an elastic band and two pencils to make a catapult, or a straw to make a peashooter.

These are fun uses of objects that are intended for a completely different purpose. Can you come up with alternative uses for each of the following sets of objects?

Again, there are no correct answers – it's up to you and your imagination!

1 A ruler and two erasers

2 A hair and a piece of sticky tape

3 A pencil case and some confetti

4 An orange, a lemon and an apple

3   Acronyms

Sometimes we shorten common sequences of words by writing just their initials. These are called 'acronyms', and it's particularly common with names of organisations.

For example, the United Nations is known as the 'UN', and that's an acronym: it's made up of the first letter of each word in the name. You can make up your own acronyms, too, which only you know. For example, if RAT were an acronym related to schools, it could stand for Really Annoying Teacher! Here are some topics with potential acronyms. Can you suggest what they might stand for?
It's entirely up to you!

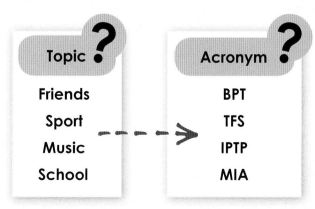

Topic ?	Acronym ?
Friends	BPT
Sport	TFS
Music	IPTP
School	MIA

Need help with solving these puzzles? Turn to pages 26 to 28 for helpful tips.

Riddles

A riddle is a word puzzle that can be solved by a clever interpretation of the question, sometimes by looking at different ways to use a word or concept involved. You can solve them by thinking carefully and looking out for cunning tricks!

1 It's a riddle

Consider the saying...

"There's no 'I' in 'team'. "

This is sometimes used to illustrate that everyone in a team should work together and not as an individual. It's witty because there really is no letter 'i' in the word 'team'. Of course, it's not actually correct English, but people get away with saying it because it's clearly intended as a joke.

Riddles can sometimes be a bit like this, with multiple meanings. Here's an example:

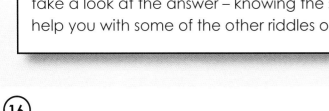

"What word is always spelled incorrectly?"

Think about the exact meaning of this question. Is there a trick in there to make it much easier than it first appears? If you're stuck, check the tips section. And if you're still stuck, take a look at the answer – knowing the solution might help you with some of the other riddles on these pages!

2 Riddle me this

1. What is made by light and yet is always dark?

2. What goes up when rain comes down?

 **3.** What word becomes shorter when you add two letters to it?

4. What has an eye but cannot see?

5. What can you catch but cannot throw back?

6. The more it dries, the wetter it becomes. What is it?

7. What is so delicate that just saying its name breaks it?

Need help with solving these puzzles? Turn to pages 26 to 28 for helpful tips.

Lateral Thinking

You've already tried out your logical puzzle-solving and number skills, and experimented with creative inventions. So how good are you at putting together your logical thoughts and creative ideas to solve seemingly impossible problems?

1 Clothes issues

1. Have a think about this problem:

If I pick up a scarf, how can I tie a knot in it without letting go of either end?

Does it sound impossible? It isn't. There is an easy solution that you could try out yourself with a scarf, tea towel, handkerchief, or any piece of material you can tie a knot in!

You're not allowed to let go at any time after you pick it up. Thinking about that, is there something you can do before you pick it up that would allow you to tie the knot?

You don't need to do anything to the scarf first – it's all about the way you pick it up.

2. Here's another lateral-thinking puzzle on clothing. You might come up with more than one solution, but there's a particularly simple way to solve it.

While wearing a pair of trousers, how can I put my left hand into the right pocket and my right hand into the left pocket without crossing my arms?

If you think the answer is to put one hand behind your back, you'll probably find if you try it that you can't actually do that! There's at least one other method to discover.

More lateral thinking

All of these problems relate to time. How long will it take you to come up with solutions?

Can you solve this? It sounds unlikely, but there's an easy explanation if you can find it.

1. The day before yesterday I was 8 years old. Next year I will be 11 years old. How can this be true?

This is a much more sneaky one! It might not be entirely to do with time.

2. Cowboy Bill rode into town on Friday. Then he rode out two days later on Friday. How is this possible?

This requires you to think about the extremes of the Earth!

3. Between sunset and sunrise I got out of bed 120 times, and yet I managed to sleep over 8 hours between every single time that I got up. How can you explain that?

Finally, another riddle that may or may not really be about time.

4. If I tell you that I know someone who predicts the future, how can I possibly be telling the truth?

Need help with solving these puzzles? Turn to pages 26 to 28 for helpful tips.

More Lateral Thinking

The lateral-thinking puzzles on these pages are designed to make you think. Solutions are given at the back of the book, but the idea is to get your creative juices flowing – so whatever solution you come up with each time is perfectly acceptable, as long as it works. There's not always just one right answer!

1 Lateral-thinking problems

1. What occurs once in January and once in February, but then doesn't occur again until June, July and August?

2. I have a bottle of lemonade that I've started drinking.

There's more than half left but I've promised to leave exactly half the bottle for my brother.

How can I be sure to do this, without using any other item to measure it?

3. A proud father gave his son a pair of engraved pens, and a different proud father gave his son a set of four pens. Yet there were only four pens in total between both sons. How can this be true?

4. I'm holding a horse race but I want there to be a twist to the usual proceedings: the horse that comes in last will win. However, I don't want the race to go on forever, so what can I do to persuade the jockeys to ride normally?

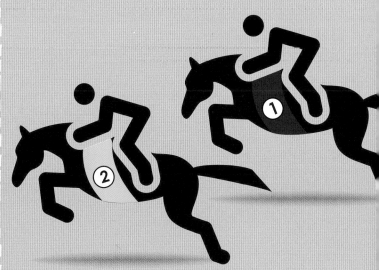

5. My pet hamster has got stuck in a hole in the ground, and I can't reach in to get it out. Can you think of a simple way to get it out without hurting it?

6. If the Sea of Tranquillity is on the Moon and the Black Sea is on Earth, on which planet is the Red Sea?

Need help with solving these puzzles? Turn to pages 26 to 28 for helpful tips.

21

Even More Lateral Thinking

All of the lateral-thinking problems on these two pages have something to do with numbers. Some of them might even involve a bit of maths, but look out for those that have much sneakier answers!

1 Lateral-thinking problems

1. We can all agree that one comes before two, but how can two come after three and four before one?

2. Imagine that you place two identical coins on the table so that they are touching side-by-side.

Now imagine that you hold the first coin down with your finger, and roll the second coin all the way around the outside of the first coin, keeping it touching at all times.

How many complete revolutions will the second coin have turned through by the time it gets back to where it started? Try and work it out without using coins first.

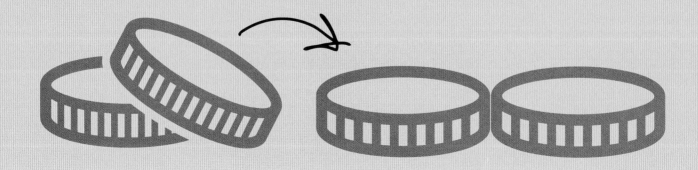

3. How can you stand over a bare concrete floor and drop an uncooked egg a distance of a metre without it breaking? You cannot modify the egg in any way.

4. If Tom the tabby cat drinks precisely half of his saucer of milk every day, and none of the remaining milk evaporates or is removed, how long will it take him to finish a saucer containing a pint of milk?

5. If I pick up a spherical ball and mark any three points on it, what is the chance that all three points end up on the same half of the ball?

6. If I go for a walk into a forest, what is the furthest distance I can get from the edge of the forest, expressed as a fraction of the entire width of the forest?

Need help with solving these puzzles? Turn to pages 26 to 28 for helpful tips.

Language Games

If you've worked your way through the various puzzles in this book, you'll definitely be primed for some seriously creative thinking. These pages feature a few different creative activities you can try to test out your powers!

1 Fridge magnets

You might have seen, or even have, a fridge covered in magnetic letters that you can rearrange to make words.

In this advanced version of the activity, the fridge displays words instead of letters for you to arrange.

Have a look at the fridge, then see what you can come up with!

The more creative the better!

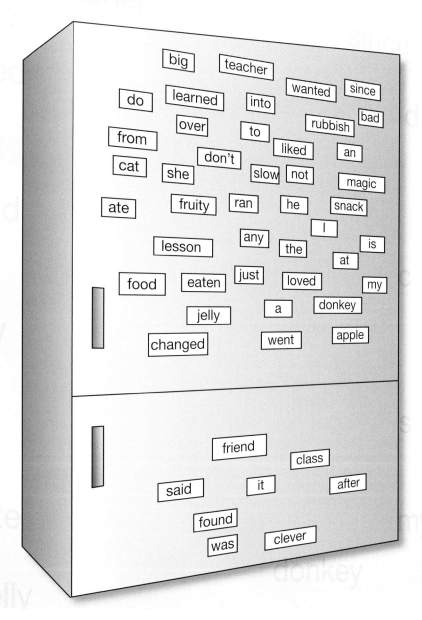

2 Starting letters

Can you think of a country of the world starting with each letter of the alphabet in turn? It's not so hard to think of Australia or Austria for A, for example, but can you do the same for every letter of the alphabet? There is at least one country beginning with every letter, except for X!

Here are some other lists you can try. You might not be able to find an item starting with every letter, but see how many you can manage!

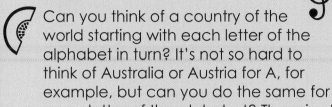

Musical instruments

Movies

Fruit and vegetables

Boys' names

Girls' names

Five-letter words

Sports teams

Football players

Brand names

Shop names

TV shows

3 Explain this

Here's a simple creative game that only needs two dice to play. Just roll both dice once for each column, and then explain the 'Where, What and Who' situation as creatively as you can! In each case you have a place, an object and a person or group of people. Can you find an explanation for why that person or group has that object in that place? Some dice rolls will give easier tasks than others! For example, if you roll a total of 7 the first time, the place is 'school'. If you roll 3 the second time, the object is 'a ruler'. On your third roll, a 12 would give you 'your best friend'. So can you explain what your best friend would be doing with a ruler at school? That one might be quite easy, but the chances are you'll come up with some that are much harder to explain! Be as creative as you like!

	Dice roll 1 – Where?	Dice roll 2 – What?	Dice roll 3 – Who?
2	At a friend's house	A picture of the moon	A sports team
3	At your house	A ruler	Your family
4	On a bus	A football	The head teacher
5	In the park	A bat	A politician
6	At the shops	Your sports kit	A waiter
7	At school	A piece of fruit	A shop assistant
8	On the football field	An alarm clock	An alien
9	In the playground	A sandwich	A famous sports star
10	At a museum	A measuring jug	A movie star
11	At a party	A baseball cap	Your teacher
12	At church	A sewing machine	Your best friend

Need help with solving these puzzles? Turn to pages 26 to 28 for helpful tips.

Helpful Tips

Page 5   Introduction

Have a closer look at the words used in the question.

Pages 6 – 7

Numbers and Reasoning

Tricks with numbers

A good way to see how these tricks work is to follow them through with different ages or numbers, and see what happens in each case. Can you work out how each different starting number gives you the same end result after following the instructions?

Pouring problem

The secret is to work out step by step how to obtain different volumes of liquid. You start with 8 litres in container C.

If you pour as much as you can into B, you will have 5 litres in B and 3 litres in C. Now if you pour as much as you can from B into A, you will have 2 litres in B. So you now know you can obtain an exact volume of 2 litres, as well as 3, 5 and 8 litres. You can also think about what's missing from each container. For example, if you had the 2 litres in A, you could subtract exactly 1 litre from either B or C by filling up A.

River crossing

The secret of this puzzle is to remember that you can bring things across the river **and** bring them back again. You can work out from the rules that you can't leave the cat with any other item on either side of the river.

Pages 8 – 9

Number Manipulation

Number anagrams

You know you can only multiply or add, or in the second challenge, subtract as well, so if you are stuck then pick two numbers of your choice and try adding or multiplying them. Now what do you need to do to get to the solution? Has this helped? If not, try again with another pair of numbers. Think about your times tables and how you can get close to the result you need. Is there something you can multiply to get there? How about if you add two numbers, then multiply the result?

Number sequences

These work in a similar way to the example, except for the last one. There is a relationship here where each number is based on the two before it – can you see what it is?

Brain chains

If you find it difficult to remember the partial results as you go then try writing down the answer to each step on a separate piece of paper.

Pages 10 – 11   Find the Numbers

How old?

The easiest way to tackle this is to guess at some of the children's ages and see how close to a valid answer you are, then make small changes to their ages until you find the solution.

Street map

Look at the picture and note the three house numbers that are given. There are only three options, so there aren't many possibilities to try. You don't need to guess. Try starting with the clues that involve the least number of people, such as the last one. What possibilities are there for the house numbers of Gayatri and Eliza?

Page 11

Find the Numbers

Balloon bursting

Start by adding up all of the balloons. From this, work out the total you would need to burst in each case. Once you've done that, you'll see that you only need to burst one balloon to end up with a total of 44, and that you'll need to burst more than one balloon to make the other totals.

Pages 12 – 13

Amazing Numbers

Super-Secret code

You'll definitely find this easier if you write out the reverse-alphabet code first!

Ultra-secret code

The secret here is to think about the addition that has been applied. To undo the addition you must subtract something, and that something is the **decoded** number of each letter.

Maths genius (You try it!)

All of the questions can be answered by applying the rules further up the page. Don't use a calculator to do these!

Pages 14 – 15

Open to Interpretation

Hidden in plain sight

There are no correct answers here. If you can't think of anything, you could start by looking for objects that are the same colour as the background of the picture. For example, in the first picture the background is green. What can you think of that's coloured green? Grass, perhaps? Leaves?

But what's it for?

What's great here is that you can't possibly be wrong because there is no right answer! If you can't think of anything, try finding the actual items and playing about with them. Does anything come to mind now?

Acronyms

You don't need to think of something that fits all the letters straight away. Try thinking of a word that starts with one of the letters – maybe B could be for 'Best' in the Friends topic – then see if you can come up with ideas for the other letters. It doesn't matter if they sound silly!

Pages 16 – 17

Riddles

It's a riddle

This one is about words and their spelling – so what word would you spell 'incorrectly'?

Riddle me this

1) If you shine a light on an object, what can you see behind the object?
2) When it rains, what might someone put up?
3) What happens if you remove two letters from 'shorter'?
4) Can you think of any objects that have an 'eye'?
5) If you stay out in the wet without a coat, what might you catch?
6) What can you use to dry things?
7) When you talk in a quiet room, what is it said that you break?

Page 18

Lateral Thinking

Clothes issues

1) If you can't let go of it, then can you do something with your arms before you pick it up?
2) This is physically very hard, if not impossible. So is there something you can perhaps do to the trousers to make it easier?

Page 19 **Lateral Thinking**

More lateral thinking

1) Think about what day it might be today. It's probably at the very start or end of the year, isn't it?
2) 'Cowboy Bill' is capitalized because it's a name. What other words are capitalized?
3) Is there somewhere on Earth where this might actually be possible, where it is dark for a very long time?
4) Have a very close look at the exact words in the question. What is definitely true in what I am saying?

Pages 20 – 21 **More Lateral Thinking**

Lateral-thinking problems

1) The solution to this has something to do with the words!
2) Do you have a lid for the bottle? If so, the bottle doesn't have to be standing upright, does it?
3) Imagine that you are one of the sons. Can you think of a way in which the situation could be true? Is it possible that the other son in the story could be related to you too?
4) If we assume that each jockey wants to win, what can they do to make sure that another horse finishes before their own?
5) Is there some way to fill in the hole without trapping the hamster at the same time?
6) Whether you find this question tricky or not depends on your general knowledge…

Pages 22 – 23 **Even More Lateral Thinking**

Lateral-thinking problems

1) Notice that in this question the numbers are written as words. Do you think that's relevant?
2) Once the second coin has travelled half way around the first one, you might expect it to have turned through half a revolution – but will it have? Are you sure?
3) Read the question carefully. You might be misunderstanding exactly what is being asked!
4) If half is always left, what effect will this have on the answer to the question?

5) This can be quite tricky, but try to imagine that you're holding a ball in your hands. Think about three points on it. Can you picture if they could all be on one half of the ball?
6) You know that a fraction tells you how much of something you have, which in this case is how far across the width of the forest you've travelled. For example, you could go a quarter of the way into the forest. How far, as a fraction, would you be from the far side at that point? And at what point in are you furthest from either edge of the forest?

Pages 24 – 25 **Language Games**

Fridge magnets

If you're short of inspiration, just put your finger on the page without looking and take that as your starting word! What can come next?

Starting letters

If you find this tricky, get some friends to help. It's funny how things like this are much easier in a group, and everyone is smarter as a whole than they are individually! It's because you'll all have different bits of knowledge, and so the sum of everything you know together is usually more than what any of you knows on your own.

Explain this!

If you can't think of an explanation for your dice roll, just roll again! It's meant to be fun after all. This game is best played with friends – see who can think up the funniest explanation!

Answers

Introduction

What occurs once in a minute, twice in a moment but not once in a thousand years? The letter 'm'!

Pages 6 – 7

Numbers and Reasoning

Tricks with numbers

You can see how the first trick works by using a label for your age. If we say your age is 'a', we can write everything out a bit more compactly. If we double your age, we get 'a x 2'. Now we add 6, which gives 'a x 2 + 6'. Then we divide it by 2, which means we take half of the 'a x 2', which is

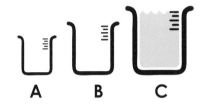

of course just 'a' again, and half of the 6, which is 3. So we now have 'a + 3'. Then we subtract your age again, which leaves us with just 3. And that's how it works! You can come up with similar mathematical routines to make up your own number tricks.

The second trick relies on the fact that any multiple of 9 has digits which also add up to a multiple of 9. You can check this for yourself, from 1 x 9 through to 10 x 9, giving 9, 18, 27, 36, 45, 54, 63, 72, 81, 90. We ask you to think of a number from 1 to 9 and add 1, so you're really thinking of a number from 2 to 10. As you can see, all of these when multiplied by 9 have two digits that add up to 9. Therefore when you add on 6, you are certain to get 15 – easy!

Pouring problem

The solution requires 7 steps:
- Pour C into B so you now have A = 0, B = 5, C = 3
- Pour B into A for 3, 2, 3
- Pour A into C for 0, 2, 6
- Pour B into A for 2, 0, 6
- Pour C into B for 2, 5, 1
- Pour B into A for 3, 4, 1
- Pour A into C for 0, 4, 4

River crossing

First bring over the cat, as it can't be left with the dog or the cat food. Then go back and get either the dog or the cat food. Here's the trick: when you get to the far bank again, **bring back the cat to the first side**. Then you can bring over the dog or cat food, whichever you left behind. Go back a third time to get the cat. Done!

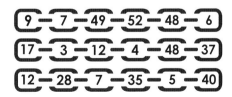

Pages 8 – 9

Number Manipulation

Number anagrams

$19 = 7 \times 2 + 5$ $13 = 3 \times 4 + 7 - 6$
$37 = 5 \times 7 + 2$ $15 = 3 \times 6 + 4 - 7$
$49 = (5 + 2) \times 7$ $34 = (3 + 7) \times 4 - 6$

(The brackets make it clear that you add the 5 and 2 first before multiplying by 7.)

Number sequences

2 5 8 11 14 17 20
(add 3 at each step)

27 23 19 15 11 7 3
(subtract 4 at each step)

1 2 4 8 16 32 64
(multiply by 2 at each step)

1 2 3 5 8 13 21 (add the two previous numbers at each step)

Brain chains

9 — 7 — 49 — 52 — 48 — 6

17 — 3 — 12 — 4 — 48 — 37

12 — 28 — 7 — 35 — 5 — 40

Pages 10 – 11 Find the Numbers

How old?

Andrew is 5, Bradley is 7 and Corey is 12.

Street map

Let's call the children by their initials: D, E, F, G and H. We know that E + D = 12, so given we have the numbers 5, 7 and 9 to choose from, this means that either E = 5 and D = 7, or E = 7 and D = 5. We also know that E + G = 14, so either E = 5 and G = 9, or E = 9 and G = 5. But we already know that E can only be 5 or 7, so it must be E = 5 and G = 9. This also means that D = 7. So that's three children assigned to a house! Next, we know that H + G + E + D = 26, and since we know the values of G, E and D, we can be sure that H = 5. Finally, we know that F + H + D = 19, and given we already know D and H, then this means F = 7. So the answer is: Eliza and Hayden – number 5

Dan and Frankie – number 7

Gayatri – number 9

Balloon bursting

- 44 – burst 5
- 35 – burst 4 & 10
- 19 – burst 13 & 17
- 18 – burst 4, 10 & 17

Secret code

WELL DONE

Super-secret code

CODE CRACKED

Ultra-secret code This is more complex to decode because you need to do some subtraction! We start with the first letter, 7, which we know is T (since T = 7, U = 6, V = 5, W = 4, X = 3, Y = 2 and Z = 1). Then we subtract the 7 from the next number, 13, to give 6. We know that 6 is U. Next is a tricky bit, since we subtract the **decoded number,** i.e. "6", from the next number, 28, to give 22, "E". We carry on like this until we read the entire code, which reveals the day TUESDAY.

Maths genius (You try it!)

- **A multiple of 2?** No, because it doesn't end in an even number.
- **A multiple of 3?** Yes, because the digits sum to 39, which is a multiple of 3. If you're not sure, you can sum the digits of 39 to get 12, which you know is 4 x 3.
- **A multiple of 4?** Yes, because 24 is 6 x 4. $\sqrt{a^2} = |a|$
- **A multiple of 5?** Yes, because it ends in a 0 or a 5.
- **A multiple of 6?** No, because it does not end in an even number, even though it is actually a multiple of 3.

Page 15 Open to Interpretation

But what's it for?

There are no correct answers for this, but here are some ideas!

1) You could make a seesaw with one eraser and the ruler, then put the other eraser on one end of the seesaw and punch down on the opposite end to send it flying across the room!

2) You could make a trap to see if anyone's been in your room. Tape across a closed door would be obvious, but if you tape a hair across your door instead, then if someone goes into your room they'll dislodge the hair without noticing they've set off your trap!

3) You could put the confetti in the pencil case and then balance it on top of a door to catch the unwary … but only do this with a cloth pencil case!

4) You could try juggling the fruit!

Acronyms

There are no correct answers for this either, but here are some possibilities to get you going if you can't think of anything!

Acronym	Topic	Suggestion
BPT	Friends	Birthday Party Tonight
TFS	Sport	This Footballer Stinks
IPTP	Music	I Play The Piano
MIA	School	Maths Is Awesome

Page 16 Riddles

It's a riddle

The word 'incorrectly' is always spelled incorrectly, isn't it?

Page 17 Riddles

Riddle me this

1. A shadow! You might also think up other answers.
2. An umbrella, and again you can probably think of other answers to do with rain.
3. 'Short' becomes 'shorter' when you add the two letters 'er'!
4. A needle. Or you might have said a potato, and you can find other answers to this, too.
5. A cold. Or perhaps something that is about to destroy itself in some way, but a cold is the classic answer to this riddle!
6. A towel!
7. Silence! If you speak in a quiet room you 'break' the silence.

Pages 20 – 21 More Lateral Thinking

Lateral thinking problems

1. This is another word one – it's the letter 'u'!
2. If you put the bottle flat on its side (with the lid on!), you can easily see whether it is still more than half full. You can keep checking in this way until the bottle is precisely half full.
3. One fathers was the son of the other father, so he just passed on the two pens his own father had already given him, plus two more of his own.
4. You get the jockeys to swap horses with each other, and as each still wants their own horse to win, they will try to beat it by riding normally.
5. One method is to pour in sand (slowly!) until the hamster can climb out by itself.
6. Earth! The question is written in such a way as to encourage the incorrect answer 'Mars', since Mars is known as the Red Planet due to its colour.

Pages 22 – 23 Even More Lateral Thinking

Lateral thinking problems

1. They do in a dictionary! In other words, when sorted alphabetically, we have four, one, three, two.
2. The outer coin will perform two full revolutions.
3. You simply catch the egg after dropping it.
4. The normal answer to this question is that it will take him forever, since as the question is defined he always leaves half – and if he always leaves half, then he can't ever finish it! Of course, in the real world this isn't what would happen.
5. It's a certainty – try it out! There will always be one half of the ball where all your points are.
6. Half the width of the forest. Once you've walked more than halfway into the forest, you'll start getting closer to the far edge instead!

Pages 18 – 19 Lateral Thinking

Clothes issues

1. Start, without holding the scarf, by folding your arms. Now take your right hand and move it from underneath your left arm so that it is resting on top of your left arm, keeping your arms otherwise as they were. Grab the scarf with both hands and uncross your arms – and it will be knotted!
2. Put the trousers on back to front, so the right and left pockets swap positions!

Pages 20 – 21 More Lateral Thinking

1. It's 1st January today, and my birthday is on 31st December. I'm 9 years old today, but the day before yesterday, 30th December, I was still 8. At the end of this year, on 31st December, I will turn 10, and the year after ('next year') I will have my 11th birthday on 31st December.
2. Cowboy Bill's **horse's name** is Friday!
3. I must be living in or near the Arctic or Antarctic, where there is no daylight in winter! The sun never rises during this time.
4. I say that my friend predicts the future, but when I say I am telling the truth I'm not **also** saying that my friend predicts the future **accurately** – I'm just saying that they **predict** it.

Index

About the Author

Dr. Gareth Moore is the author of a wide range of puzzle and brain-training books for both children and adults, including The Kids' Book of Puzzles, The Mammoth Book of Brain Games and The Rough Guide Book of Brain Training. He is also the founder of daily brain training site **www.BrainedUp.com**. He gained his Ph.D from Cambridge University (UK) in the field of computer speech recognition, teaching machines to understand spoken words.